Wit & Humour

The Best of

Gopal & Paramanand

Wit & Humour - The Best of Gopal & Paramanand
ISBN 81-88759-08-2

Published by

SPIDER BOOKS
AH-73/1, 7th Main Road, Shanthi Colony
Anna Nagar, Chennai - 600 040 (INDIA)
Phone: 044-42171048 / 32934340
E-mail: spider@spiderbooks.net

Reprinted 2005
Reprinted 2006
Reprinted 2007

Retold by
Brian Jude
Illustrations
V.K.Santhosh

Printed in India

Contents

Introduction

A long time ago, in the ancient land of Bengal, there lived a barber called Gopal Bhand.

Gopal was a clever and witty barber, who became very popular with the local people. They would often turn to him to help them escape from a difficult situation, or to solve a difficult problem.

Gopal lived in a small Kingdom, ruled by a very weak King called Raja Krishna Chandra. The King did not have a strong army and had to seek protection from the great Nawab of Murshidabad. The Nawab was a short-tempered fellow who would often give the poor Raja Krishna Chandra difficult tasks. He would threaten to stop protecting the Raja if he did not complete the tasks.

The Raja often turned to Gopal to help him solve the difficult tasks that were given to him. This lead Gopal into many fantastic adventures that became legendary stories.

The Miser's Haircut

In the town where Gopal lived, there was a very miserly man. He would always try and find an excuse not to pay people for things that he bought from them. He would go to a hotel, eat some of the food that the waiter served him, and then he would get up and say, "I don't like the food. I am not going to pay for it." He would go to a vegetable shop, buy one kilo of vegetables, leave a few vegetables behind and tell the vegetable man that he would pay for it when he picks it up.

Many people complained to Raja Krishna, asking him to put the miser in prison. As usual, Raja Krishna did not know what to do, so he called his trusted friend, Gopal the barber and said to him, "Gopal! This miser is a very tricky fellow. You must do something to teach him a lesson."

So Gopal waited for the right opportunity to teach the miser a lesson. A week later he got that opportunity.

The miser decided that he wanted to get a haircut. Since Gopal was the only barber in town, he had to come to Gopal's shop.

The miser had already decided not to pay Gopal for the haircut. He said to Gopal, "I hear that you are the greatest barber in the world. I would like to challenge you to prove it to me. I want you to cut my hair so that every hair on my head is the same length."

Gopal knew that the miser was trying to trick him, so he listened carefully. The miser continued, "But remember, if even one hair is longer than the other, I will not pay you for the haircut."

Gopal accepted the challenge and began to cut the miser's hair. As was the custom in those parts of the country, the barber would first massage the head and then cut the hair.

As Gopal massaged the miser's head, the miser fell asleep.

When he awoke, the miser looked into the mirror and shouted out, "What! What have you done? You fool!"

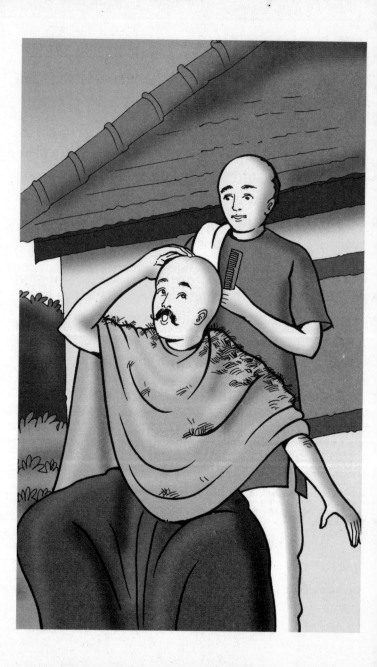

The miser found that Gopal had shaved his head completely.

Gopal smiled and said, "You wanted me to cut your hair in such a way that every hair on your head was of the same size, well this is how I did it."

Now keep your promise and pay me, or else I will report you to the King."

The miser knew that he had been outwitted by the clever Gopal. He had to pay Gopal the money, and from that day onward, he stopped being a miser.

Counting The Stars

Gopal helped King Raja Krishna on many occasions. One day when he went to see the King, he found the King looking very sad. Gopal said to him, "Why are you looking so sad O King? Can I help you in some way?"

The King said to Gopal, "Oh! I wish you could Gopal. But I am faced with a task that would be impossible for even you to solve."

Gopal smiled and said, "At least let me give it a try O King! You know that I love a challenge."

King Raja Krishna sighed and said, "The Nawab is troubling me once again. Every once in a while he gives me an impossible task. He threatens me, telling me that if I don't complete the task, he will stop protecting our Kingdom."

Gopal became very interested and asked the King, "What is this task, please tell me!" The King answered, "You won't believe it. He has asked me to count all the stars that we see over our

Kingdom. When I asked him why, he said that he wanted to count them because he wanted to make sure that none of them ran away from our Kingdom!"

Gopal laughed and then thought for a while. Suddenly an idea struck him. He said to King Raja Krishna, "I think I know how to outwit him O King. Just give me a flock of sheep and I will do the rest.

The King did not understand what Gopal was trying to do, but he trusted Gopal, so he gave him a flock of Royal Sheep.

Gopal found out when the Nawab went out riding in the forest nearby and took the flock of sheep there.

The Nawab went riding in the forest to relax. He always had his guards and two of his ministers with him.

When they rode into the forest they were surprised to see a man, right in the middle of a flock of sheep. They did not know that the man was Gopal, the witty barber.

As they got closer they saw that the man was carefully looking into the hair of the sheep. He was counting loudly, "Two Thousand Five Hundred and Sixty Six, Two Thousand Five Hundred and Sixty Seven, Two Thousand Five Hundred and Sixty Eight, Two Thousand Five Hundred and Sixty Nine…"

The Nawab rode up to him and said, "Hey you! What are you doing?"

Gopal looked up and said, "Greetings Sir! I am doing what I usually do. I am counting the hairs on my flock of sheep." The Nawab, his ministers and the guards laughed out loudly and said, "Ha! Ha! Why are you counting the hairs on your sheep?"

Gopal replied, "I want to make sure that none of the hair leave my sheep and run away." The Nawab laughed once again and said, "You are a fool man! How could you count the hairs on your sheep? Don't you realise that there are too many of them and most importantly, don't you know that they can't run away. You fool! Ha! Ha!"

Gopal smiled and said, "Oh Sir! I know that I am a fool. But I know that I am not alone. I am following the example of another fool I came to hear about. I don't know who he is, but I believe he asked a King to count the number of stars in the sky, because he did not want them to run away."

The Nawab stopped laughing, but his ministers and the guards burst out laughing louder. They knew that the Nawab had asked King Raja to count the stars. The Nawab was angry and shouted at his ministers and the guards, "Shut up! Stop laughing!"

Then he turned to Gopal and said, "So you don't know who asked the King to count the stars right?" Gopal answered, "Yes Sir! But I plan to find out. He was the one who inspired me to count the hairs on my sheep." Without uttering another word the Nawab turned his horse around and rode away shouting to his ministers and the guards, "Come on! We have got to get back to the palace now! I have to send a message to King Raja Krishna."

As soon as he got back to the palace the Nawab sent a message to King Raja Krishna. The message read, 'Dear Raja Krishna. You need not count the stars in the sky. I am not a fool. I know that there are too many stars and they can't be counted. I was just testing your loyalty to me. I am satisfied that you tried. You may stop trying to count the stars.'

King Raja Krishna was overjoyed when he received the message. Just then Gopal entered the King's palace. He told the King what he had done.

King Raja Krishna was so happy that he gave Gopal a bag of gold coins and said, "Gopal! You have saved me once again. Thank you!"

Horse Tails

Gopal had worked very hard for many months and decided that he wanted to take a break and visit some of his family members in another city. So after telling the King and all his friends, Gopal climbed onto his horse and rode away.

On the way to the city where his family lived, Gopal had to pass through a small town. When he reached the town he was surprised to meet some old friends of his. When they saw him they shouted, "Hey! Gopal! How are you man?" It has been such a long time since we saw you. How are you? How is business going?"

Gopal told them all about the way he had helped King Raja Krishna and the people in his town. Since they were meeting after many years Gopal decided to sat in the town and spend some time with his friends. Throughout the day Gopal and his friends ate, drank, dance and made merry. Making up for all the time they had lost. They were friends from the school days.

After a few days Gopal suddenly realised that he had used up all the money he had. He had planned to give some money to his family members. But now he had nothing.

He said to his friends, "Hey guys! It looks like I have used up all my money. Would any of you be able to lend me some money? I will give it back to you once I return home?"

His friends replied, "Oh! Gopal! Just like you, we have also used up all our money!" Gopal thought for a while and then said, "Ah! I have an idea that will help me earn some money." Saying that he rode off to the town square. During the night, he set up a small tent in the town square and put his horse inside it.

The next day Gopal waited till the town square was filled with people who had come there to do some shopping. Then Gopal stood up on a chair and shouted, "Hey people! Are you ready to see an amazing sight! Come here! Come here! All of you who want to see an amazing sight!" Soon a crowd of people gathered around Gopal. Gopal shouted, "This is like nothing you've ever seen people! Come here and see a horse that has its head, where its tail ought to be and its head where its tail ought to be!"

The people gasped in amazement. They had never seen a horse that had a head where its tail ought to be and a head where its tail ought to be.

More people gathered around Gopal and the tent. Gopal shouted, "I am not going to charge you a price to see this amazing sight, but I would like you to be generous and contribute whatever you can. You see I am a poor man and I need to feed this strange horse!" The people contributed money willingly, and soon Gopal had a bag full of money. Then he shouted, "Ok! Stand back and get ready to see an amazing sight!" The people moved back as Gopal opened the tent!

They were shocked to see Gopal's horse had a tail where its head should have been and a head where its tail should have been.

Suddenly one of them burst out laughing and shouted! "Ha! Ha! What a wonderful trick! This

man has tied his horse up to a post by its tail, thus making us think that it was the head!"

All the people burst out laughing, as they realised that the witty and clever Gopal had tricked them cleverly.

Gopal asked them if they wanted their money back. But everyone said, "You are a very clever and witty man! You made us laugh in the morning. You deserve the money."

Gopal was very happy and rode away to meet his family members with a lot more money than he had when he entered the town.

To Trick A Thief

The city where Gopal lived was suddenly gripped by fear. A gang of thieves had robbed three houses in one week. No one could catch them because they were fast. They broke into homes at night and ran away with all the jewels and money in the house. People were afraid of them and King Raja Krishna offered a reward for anyone who could catch them.

One night when Gopal and his wife were sleeping, they heard someone banging on the window. Gopal's wife woke him up and shouted, "Gopal! Gopal! I think that the gang of thieves! They have come to rob us!" Gopal got up and was about to reach for a stick when there was a crashing sound. Gopal and his wife were surprised to find only one thief enter their house through the window. The thief was holding a knife, so Gopal decided not to try and fight him. The thief shouted, "Don't try anything funny now! Just give me all your jewellery and I will not hurt you."

Gopal said to the thief, "Are you a part of the gang of robbers that have been robbing houses in the city?" The thief smiled and said, "Nah! I am just a local thief. I know that people will think that I am a part of the gang, that's why I began robbing small houses. Now stop talking and give me your jewels." Just as Gopal was about to go into the next room and take out the jewels, they heard a banging sound on the door.

Gopal, his wife and the thief looked scared as the banging sound became louder. Someone was trying to break down the front door. The thief who was inside the house became very afraid and said, "Hey! I think the gang of thieves are trying to get into your house. If they find me here they will surely kill me. What shall I do?"

Gopal knew that this was his opportunity. He looked at the thief and said, "Don't worry, we will protect you. Just hide under the bed and don't come out whatever happens."

The thief quickly hid himself under the bed. Gopal called his wife aside and said to her, "I am going out the back door to get help. Don't be

afraid and just do as I say." He whispered something in his wife's ear and quickly went out the back door to go and get the guards. The front door came crashing down and five very rough looking thieves entered the house, carrying knives and clubs. To their surprise they found Gopal's wife huddled in a corner. One of them shouted, "What! There is only a woman in the house? Where is the man?"

Another thief rushed up to Gopal's wife and said, "Hey you! Give us all your jewels or we will kill you!" Gopal's wife cried out helplessly, "Oh! Please don't kill me! Please don't kill me! But I can't give you the jewels because they are locked up." The thief shouted, "What? Locked up? Who has the key?" Gopal's wife cried out, "The man of the house has the key!" The thief growled, "Where is he? Tell me or I will kill you!" Gopal's wife quickly pointed to the bed and said, "He is hiding under the bed!"

The thief cried out, "What a coward! He leaves his wife out here and hides under the bed! Let's get him."

The thieves lifted the bed and pulled the helpless thief out. He cried out, "Hey! Hey! I am not the man of the house! And that woman is not my wife! I don't have the keys! She is lying!"

The thieves began to beat the other thief up shouting, "What a coward! First you hide under the bed then you say that this woman is not your wife! Cowards like you should be beaten to death!" They continued to kick and beat the thief as he cried out.

Just then Gopal arrived at the front door with ten of the King's guards, armed to the teeth. They rushed in to capture the gang of thieves. The gang was caught by surprise. The guards attacked them and soon had them on the floor tied up.

The head guard said, "Gopal you are indeed very clever. You have managed to capture this fierce gang of thieves that have been escaping us for months. Thank you! I shall see to it that the King gives you a reward."

Then noticing the first thief who was lying on the floor, bruised and beaten up he asked, "Who is this? Is he with the gang? Why were they beating him up? Shall we arrest him?"

Gopal replied, "Oh! Don't worry! He is a small time thief, I think he has learned his lesson."

The next day King Raja Krishna called Gopal over and gave him a reward.

The Master Dog

One day Gopal went to a sweetshop to buy some sweets. The local street dogs loved to wait near the sweetshop. People would usually throw them some small piece. Gopal loved animals, so as he passed one of the stray dogs, he patted it on its head. The doggie was very happy and wagged its tail. Gopal left it and entered the shop. The dog thought that Gopal was calling it inside the shop, so it followed him in. Just as Gopal entered the shop, followed by the dog, the shop owner spotted them.

He was just returning to the shop after buying some fresh sweets to sell. He rushed in after the dog and shouted at Gopal, "Gopal! How dare you bring your dog into my shop? Don't you know that it is dirty and full of fleas? Chase it out of the shop!" Gopal was shocked! He turned to the shop owner and said, "Hey! What makes you think that this is my dog? He is a stray dog that followed me into the shop."

The shopkeeper was not convinced, he said, "Ah! You think you are very witty, don't you? You can fool all the people in town, but you can't fool me. I know that it is your dog, because it followed you into the shop."

Gopal laughed and said, "Ha! Ha! My dear Sir! In that case the dog is your master!" The shopkeeper was shocked. He shouted, "What do you mean? How can the dog be my master?"

Gopal smiled and said, "You followed the dog into the shop right? If you think that I am the dog's master because it followed me into the shop, then the dog is your master because you followed it into the shop!"

The shopkeeper realised his mistake. He could not find any argument with Gopal's witty and clever answer, so he said, "Ok! Ok! I'm sorry." Saying that he put some sweets outside the shop and the dog ran out of the shop to eat them.

The Fish Challenge

In Gopal's city, Hilsa fish was a very popular dish. Everyone loved Hilsa fish curry, Fried Hilsa fish and Hilsa 65.

But there was a small problem. Hilsa fish was available only once a year. And for a very short time of one month. So when the fish was available, everyone talked about it.

So once when it was the Hilsa season, the entire city was buzzing with discussions. Housewives exchanged Hilsa recipes. Shopkeepers discussed the latest price of Hilsa. Fishermen talked about catching the biggest Hilsa of the season.

The King Raja Krishna was surprised to hear his courtiers discussing Hilsa instead of anything else. Finally he shouted, "Hey! I've had enough of this Hilsa thing! Hilsa! Hilsa! Everybody seems to be talking of Hilsa. I know that it is the Hilsa season, but this is too much. I want to put a stop to it."

One of the courtiers asked, "But how will you do that O King? Everybody talks about Hilsa. You can't force people to stop talking about Hilsa, can you?"

The King thought about it for a while and said, "Ha! If I can make them stop talking about it for a few minutes I will be happy. In fact I hereby announce that there is a reward of fifty gold coins for anyone who can bring the biggest Hilsa fish from the fish market to the palace. But if any of the people say anything about the fish or notice it, there will be no reward." For one week many people tried to bring a Hilsa fish to the palace, but on the way, everyone would discuss the big Hilsa that was going to the palace.

After one week Gopal decided to have the challenge. He woke up one morning, shaved off HALF of his beard, put mud all over his face and his hair, put on old clothes and wore his shirt backwards.

When his wife saw him she cried out, "Hey Gopal! What has happened to you? Have you gone mad? Why are you dressed like that?"

Gopal smiled and said, "I am going to buy the biggest Hilsa in the market and exchange it for fifty gold coins." His wife became more worried. She cried out, "What! Even the biggest Hilsa will only sell for one gold coin. How will you get FIFTY gold coins? Why are you acting like this?" Gopal just laughed and walked out of the house saying, "You will understand everything later my dear wife."

Gopal went to the fish market and picked up the biggest Hilsa available. Then he began walking towards the palace without making any effort to hide the fish. On the way people stared at him. But no one seemed to notice the big Hilsa fish. Everyone talked about Gopal. They said, "Look at Gopal! I think he has gone mad. He has shaved only half of his beard."

Another person said, "He looks dirty. I think he had too much to drink last night and he has lost his memory." When Gopal reached the palace the guards recognised him. One of them said, "Hey isn't that Gopal the barber? Why does he look like he is mad? We can't allow him to see

the King like this." One guard kept Gopal from entering the palace, while the other ran to tell the King. The King asked them to bring Gopal to him at once.

When Gopal entered the court, King Raja Krishna said, "Gopal! What has happened to you? Why are you dressed like this? Why have you shaved only half your beard? Have you lost your mind?"

Gopal laughed and said, "No! No! Your Majesty! I haven't lost my mind! I have just won your challenge."

The King was so disturbed by Gopal's appearance that he forgot all about his challenge. He asked Gopal, "What challenge are you talking about Gopal? Explain yourself!"

Gopal replied, "Remember O King, that you promised to give a reward of fifty gold coins to anyone who could bring the biggest Hilsa fish to the palace without anyone talking about it? Well I have just done that." Saying that Gopal held up the big Hilsa fish.

The King suddenly realised that Gopal was holding the biggest Hilsa fish he had ever seen. He began laughing loudly and said, "Gopal! Gopal! You are too clever for this city. Here is your reward of fifty gold coins. Now please go home and clean yourself up."

Gopal collected his reward and went home a happy man.

The Cranky Sweet Seller

Gopal was over forty years old, but he had a lot of young friends. He joined them when they were playing cricket, or mock battles. He joined them and helped them steal mangoes. The little children loved Gopal very much.

They would often run through the streets doing small errands for people. As a reward they would get small titbits to eat. But all the children did not like the Sweet Seller. He was a cranky old man. He would shout at the children and chase them away when they offered to help him.

On one or two occasions he asked them to deliver something for him, but when the children came back to collect their reward, he just laughed and chased them away. When he was not around, the Sweet Seller made his son look after the shop.

One day the Sweet Seller had to order small clay pots to put the sweets in. He had ordered twenty pots and could not carry them himself. When he saw the children running about on the streets he called out to them, "Hey you rascals! Come here! I want you guys to go to the pot maker's shop and pick up twenty clay pots. I ordered them yesterday, so they should be ready."

One of the children asked him, "If we do that will you give us some sweets as a reward Uncle?" The Sweet Seller grunted, "Ah! We'll see about that when you bring the pots. Now go get them!"

The children ran to the pot maker's house and collected the pots. Some of them carried two pots and some carried three. Careful not to break any, they returned to the Sweet Seller's shop.

The Sweet Seller collected the pots and said, "Not bad! I did not think that a bunch of naughty children could bring the pots without breaking them."

With that he turned to walk back into his shop. One of the children called out, "Uncle! Uncle! Have you forgotten! You said that you would give us some sweets as a reward. Can we have some sweets please."

The Sweet Seller turned around with a wicked grin and said, "Nah! Nah! I did not make any promise to you. I said we'd see about that later. Later is much, much later. Ha! Ha!"

He laughed and went into his shop ignoring the children who called out to him, 'Uncle! Uncle! Please give us our reward Uncle!"

When they found that the Sweet Seller was not listening to them, they walked away very sad that they had been tricked by the Sweet Seller.

On the way they spotted their favourite Uncle Gopal. When they told him what had happened, Gopal said to them, Oh! Don't worry! I'll get you your reward from the Sweet Seller."

It was just after lunch, and at this time the Sweet Seller would take a short rest. While he was sleeping, he would leave his son in charge of the shop.

Gopal and the children waited till they were sure that the Sweet Seller was fast asleep. Then Gopal said to the children, "Wait here and I will bring you sweets from the shop."

The children hid behind a mango tree as Gopal approached the Sweet Seller's son. Without saying a word Gopal just walked into the shop and began eating sweets. The Sweet Seller's son shouted, "Hey! You! Stop! You can't eat the sweets without paying for them."

Gopal replied in a whisper, "Oh! Don't worry! Your dad knows me. My name is AN-ANT. Tell your dad that AN-ANT has come to see him." The Sweet Seller's son was confused. So he shouted, "Daddy! Daddy! AN-ANT has come to you!" The Sweet Seller hated it when he was disturbed during his afternoon rest. He shouted, "Idiot! Don't disturb me. If an ant has come, chase it away."

The boy shouted, "But daddy, AN-ANT is eating our sweets! What should I do?" The Sweet Seller was furious. He shouted, "Listen boy, if an ant is eating our sweets, chase it away, or just ignore it. Stop disturbing me when I'm resting. Can't you take care of an ant?"

Gopal smiled and began picking up sweets and putting them in a mud pot. When he had

enough sweets for all the children he began to walk out of the shop, without paying anything.

The Sweet Seller's son became worried, "Daddy! Daddy! AN-Ant is taking some of our sweets and is leaving the shop without paying! What should I do?"

The Sweet Seller was really angry. He shouted, "That's it! If you call out to me one more time I'm going to come there and beat you up badly. If an ant is leaving our shop, why should you be worried? Let it go. How many sweets can an ant carry anyway? Now stay quiet!"

The Sweet Seller's son quietly watched Gopal as he walked away from the shop with sweets for the children. The children danced around their favourite Uncle Gopal, who had tricked the Sweet Seller who had tricked them.

4

Just One Question

One day a wise man was passing through the Kingdom where Gopal lived. On the way he met a merchant and said to him, "Hello! I am a wise man from the neighbouring Kingdom. I have heard stories about someone from this city. A barber called Gopal. I have heard that he is one of the most witty and intelligent people in this Kingdom. Is that true?"

The merchant replied, "Of course it is! I am a merchant and I travel to many Kingdoms. I can assure you that Gopal is one of the wittiest people I have ever know." The wise man was doubtful. He said, "I am not so sure about that. I would like to meet this Gopal and find out for myself. Where can I meet him?"

The merchant said to him, "Go to the palace of King Raja Krishna. Gopal is usually there, helping the King solve any problems he faces." So the merchant gave the wise man directions to the palace and then left. The wise man found his way to the palace and then requested the guards to take him to the King.

When he entered the court he said to the King, "Greetings O King Raja Krishna! I am a wise man in search of more wisdom. I have heard a lot about a barber called Gopal who lives in your Kingdom. I have heard that he can outwit almost anybody. Since I don't believe what people say, I would like to find out for myself."

The King replied, "Greetings wise man! I will be glad to introduce you to Gopal. He is indeed the most clever and witty man I know. You may find out for yourself. Would you like to give Gopal a challenge? I will send for him."

The King asked the guard to call Gopal who was in another room settling a problem between two shopkeepers. When Gopal entered the room the wise man thought to himself, "This man looks too simple and shy to be the clever and witty. I am sure that he will not be able to face my challenge."

The wise man smiled at Gopal and said, "Greetings Gopal! I have heard a lot about you. Are you the most clever and most witty man in this Kingdom?"

Gopal looked shy and said, "Oh! Please sir, I dare not claim to be anything. I am just a simple barber." The wise man became very worried. He knew that anyone who could be so humble was definitely hiding something great. So he said, "Let me find out for myself. I would like to ask you some questions. Will you give me answers for them?"

Gopal smiled and said, "I will try my best Sir." The wise man asked Gopal, "Would you like to answer one hundred questions that are quite easy or would you like to answer one question that is very, very tough?"

Gopal thought for a while and then said, "I would like to answer one question that is very, very tough Sir."

The wise man was surprised. He said, "Remember I will ask only one question. Just one. If you don't have an answer to it, you will lose. And I will tell everyone I meet that you are not that clever and witty. Is that Ok, or shall I ask you one hundred easy questions?"

Gopal smiled and said, "No problem Sir! You may ask me just ONE very, very tough question. If I fail to answer it, you may tell everyone that I am not that clever and witty."

The wise man shrugged his shoulders and said, "Ok! Are you ready?" Gopal nodded as the King looked at him. The King looked very worried. If Gopal was not able to answer the ONE question, the King and his entire Kingdom would look foolish. But he trusted Gopal so he waited patiently to see what would happen.

The wise man asked Gopal, "Which came first, the egg or the hen that laid the egg?" Gopal smiled and said, "Oh! That's easy. The hen came first!" The wise man was shocked at the confidence with which Gopal replied. So he asked, "How can you be so sure?"

Gopal smiled and said, "Ah! Sir! That's your second question. Remember you promised to ask me only one question. And I answered your first question already." The King and all the courtiers burst out laughing for they knew that Gopal had outwitted the wise man.

The wise man was angry that Gopal had outwitted him. But he secretly admired Gopal's quick wit and intelligence.

He left the Kingdom and from that day onwards spoke very highly of Gopal the witty barber, wherever he went.

An Earthly Measure

One morning just as Gopal had just risen from a good sleep, a guard from the palace came rushing in to see him. Gopal was still sleepy as the guard cried out, "Sir! Sir! The King wants to see you at once. He says the fate of the Kingdom and his very own life is being threatened. Please come with me at once." Gopal knew that this was definitely a real problem. The King would not disturb him this early in the morning unless it was something very serious. So he quickly had a bath, put on some clean clothes and went with the guard to the palace.

When he walked in he saw King Raja Krishna seated on his throne, with his hands on his head. He was crying. Gopal rushed up to him and said, "What is it O King? What has happened that is so terrible? How can I help you?" The King cried out, "Oh! Gopal! We are doomed! Not even you can get us out of this mess. Our Kingdom will be destroyed and I will be killed. Oh! God help us!"

Gopal calmed the King down and said, "Relax O King! First tell me what the problem is. Only then will I be able to tell you whether I can help you solve it or not."

The King stopped crying and said, "That wicked Nawab has given me another impossible task. Do you know that we have to pay him a fee not to attack us and to protect our Kingdom because our army is too small?"

Gopal said, "Yes your Majesty I know that." The King continued, "Well, every month we pay him a fee of one thousand gold coins. Till today we have always paid the fee on time. The Nawab is looking for an excuse to attack us, so he has sent me a message. In that message he has told me that this month he does not want the one thousand gold coins. Instead, as the protection fee, he wants me to get someone to measure the length and breadth of the Earth! If I don't do it, he says that he will attack our Kingdom and kill me!"

Gopal realised that the wicked Nawab just wanted to conquer King Raja Krishna's Kingdom.

He thought for a while and said, "O King! I think I know how to get us out of this problem. I want you to trust me and give me what I want."

The King sighed and said, "Gopal are you sure of what you are doing? Remember that my life and the whole Kingdom is at stake. You must not fail us!"

Gopal smiled and said, "When have I failed you O King! I would like you to give me fifteen bullock-carts filled with all the silk and cotton thread in our Kingdom."

The King ordered his guards to start collecting all the silk and cotton thread in the Kingdom and put them in fifteen bullock-carts.

After seven days the bullock-carts were filled with over five thousand balls of thread. In different sizes. Some of silk, others of cotton.

Gopal got in to the first bullock-cart and lead the rest in a line to see the Nawab. When he arrived at the Nawab's palace, Gopal stopped the fifteen bullock-carts and went in to see the Nawab.

He bowed before the Nawab and said, "Greeting O Nawab! King Raja Krishna has sent me. As per you request he asked me to measure the length and breadth of the Earth." Before he could say another word, the Nawab jumped up smiling and said, "Ah! So you have come to tell me that you could not do it right?"

Gopal smiled and said, "On the other hand O Nawab, I have come to tell you that I have finished measuring the length and breadth of the Earth. In fact, I have brought the measurements for you to check." The Nawab was shocked. He shouted, "What! But..but..that's not possible!" Gopal smiled once again and said, "I have proof O Nawab! Come with me and I will show you."

The shocked Nawab followed Gopal to the palace grounds. There he saw the fifteen bullock-carts and shouted, "What is the meaning of this?" Gopal said, "I measured the Earth with silk and cotton thread. The first eight bullock-carts contain all the thread I used to measure the breadth of the Earth. The other seven bullock-carts contain all the thread I used to measure the length of the

Earth." The Nawab looked angry and shouted, "What if the measurements are wrong?"

Gopal smiled and said, "That's why I brought them to you Sir! You can get somebody to double check. Ask them to take the thread and measure the length and breadth of the Earth once again. In fact, if you want to be sure I suggest that you do the measuring yourself!"

The Nawab did not know what to say. He had been tricked by the witty and clever Gopal. He muttered, "Er..uh…that's alright! I believe you! Tell your King that I am…er…satisfied with his effort, and that I will continue to protect his Kingdom."

Gopal rushed back to tell King Raja Krishna the good news! King Raja Krishna cried out, "Gopal! You are sent by God! Without you I would be doomed to die! Not only have you tricked the Nawab, but you have also save one thousand gold coins for our Kingdom. As a reward I will give you five hundred gold coins."

Gopal took the money and lived happily.

Say 'NO!'

Over a period of time Gopal the witty barber, became King Raja Krishna's favourite person. Gopal had helped the King on many occasions. So whenever Gopal asked the King for something, the King would immediately say 'YES!' He trusted Gopal completely.

The ministers and courtiers in King Raja Krishna's court were very jealous of Gopal.

They tried their best to make Gopal look like a fool. But every time Gopal would get the better of them and make them look like fools instead.

One day the ministers and courtiers got together and decided to talk to the King when Gopal was not around. One of them said to King Raja Krishna, "Your majesty! You trust Gopal too much. He gets away with so many things because you say YES to anything he says. If for once you say NO to whatever he says you will see that he will not be able to solve any problems for you."

The King thought about it for a while and then said, "I know that all of you are jealous of Gopal. And I know that he is a clever and witty man in spite of what you say. But I will prove to you that Gopal is clever and witty even if I don't say YES to whatever he says. Tomorrow when Gopal enters the court I will say 'NO' to whatever he says. Let's see what happens." The ministers and courtiers were very pleased with themselves.

The next day when Gopal arrived in the court he noticed that the ministers and courtiers were giggling behind his back. He realised that something was going on and decided to be careful.

The King began discussing the usual issues in the court. They discussed how to help the people in the Kingdom become more intelligent. Gopal stepped forward with a solution and said, "Why don't we ask them to have a one hour discussion on some topic every day O King?"

The King looked at Gopal and said, "No!"

Gopal was shocked because the King usually never said NO to him. So he said, "But your

Majesty, don't you think that it would help them gain confidence in themselves?"

Once again the King flatly said, "No!"

Gopal stayed quiet and watched what was happening. Every time he asked the King a question, the King said NO. It took a little while for Gopal to realise that the King was saying NO to whatever he said. He realised that this was some plan that the jealous ministers and courtiers had made to get rid of him. So Gopal waited for the right opportunity to get back at them.

When everyone was quiet he stepped forward and said to the King, "O King, you are great, but without your ministers and courtiers you would not be able to manage your Kingdom. I would request you to give them a special reward of five hundred gold coins each."

The ministers and courtiers could not believe their ears. Had Gopal gone mad? Why was he helping them make some extra money? They became very happy at the thought of getting five hundred gold coins.

But as per their instructions the King looked at Gopal and said, "No!"

The ministers and courtiers fell to the ground in sadness. Gopal continued, "If that is not possible then I would like to ask you to give your ministers and courtiers a free plot of land on the outskirts of the Kingdom."

Once again the ministers and courtiers looked happy. But once again the King shouted, "No!" The ministers and the courtiers began to cry. By now the King knew that Gopal had realised what the ministers and courtiers had planned. So he smiled and said to himself, "Ah! Now Gopal will show them that he is clever and witty even when I say NO to whatever he says."

Gopal continued, "O King I suggest that you should NOT ask your ministers and courtiers to work in the fields tomorrow." The King managed not to laugh, as he said, "No! I WILL ask them!"

The ministers fell before the King and said "Sorry O King! Sorry! We now know that Gopal is indeed clever and witty. Please forgive us!"

Before the King answered, Gopal said, "Yes O King! I think you should forgive them." The King shouted back, "No!" The Ministers and the courtiers got up and ran away. Gopal and the King burst out laughing. They knew that the jealous ministers and courtiers had learnt their lesson.

Caught Red-handed

Some time ago, Gopal the witty barber had helped King Raja Krishna capture some thieves who were terrorising the Kingdom. The thieves were locked up in a jail, but after six months they were set free. They promised the King that they would never steal again.

But they were hardened criminals. They waited for a few months and then returned to the same Kingdom disguised as sanyasis. They knew that the people in the Kingdom would never suspect that a sanyasi could be a thief. So after a while they began robbing shops and people's houses by night, and pretended to meditate during the day.

This went on for a while and finally the people complained to the King. They said, "Your Majesty, someone has got to do something about these thieves. They have robbed many people already and there is no sign that they will stop." King Raja Krishna at once summoned Gopal, his trusted friend.

When Gopal arrived, the King said, "Gopal, you stopped thieves once, I am sure that you will be able to stop them again." Gopal said, "I am honoured by the trust you have in me O King!"

The next day, Gopal asked the King to give him three statues made of pure gold. He took the statues and went to the town square. He placed the statues in the town square and shouted out to the people, "Listen! These are pure gold statues that were brought from Persia. They will bring good luck to our Kingdom. They will be left here for two weeks and then sent back to Persia."

People gathered around the statues and marvelled at them. When the crowd had grown large, Gopal said, "There is only one problem. It is said that these statues will bring good luck only if they are left unguarded at night. Only when this happens will the Gods know that there are honest people in this village." The people gasped in amazement, and one shouted, "But what about the thieves? Won't they steal this statue?"

Gopal said, "I hope they don't. The only thing I can do is to put these statues in a box made of iron bars. Hopefully that will prevent the thieves from stealing them." The thieves, disguised as sanyasis, saw what was going on. They giggled silently, for they knew that this would be the easiest robbery that they had ever done.

They waited for a few days and finally one night they went to the market-place and stole the box, containing the statues. When they got back to their hide-out in the forest, they broke open the iron bars and took out the statues. They hid the statues deep in the forest, and buried the broken box. Then they returned to the town, so that no one would suspect that they were the thieves.

The next day the people were shocked to find that the box with the gold statues was missing. News spread like wildfire, and soon someone told the King. The King called for Gopal at once.

When Gopal arrived, he looked very calm. The King said to him, "Gopal! What is the meaning of this? You have not been able to catch the thieves. And in the process you have lost three of my most valuable statues. Explain yourself."

Gopal smiled and said, "You will now find out who the thieves are O King." He said to the King, "Please pass an order that every person in the town should come and shake hands with you within the next one hour." The King did not understand what was going on in Gopal's mind so he said, "What for? I do not wish to meet my people during this bad time." Gopal said, "Please trust me O King."

The King trusted Gopal so he passed an order that every person in the Kingdom should come and shake his hand within the next one hour. Then Gopal whispered to him, "While you are shaking hands with your people, please look at the colour of their hands. The ones with red hands are the ones that stole your statue."

Soon there was a long line of people waiting outside the palace. Each one walked up to the King and shook his hand. After about forty-five minutes, the sanyasis came up to shake hands with the King. When the King shook their hands he saw that their hands were red! He shouted, "How can this be? Gopal! I think you have made

a mistake! They are sanyasis, not thieves. How could they steal the gold statues?"

Gopal said, "O King! If their hands are red, then they are the ones that stole the statues. I put the statues in a box that had iron bars. When no one was looking I covered the iron bars with red dye. Only someone who tried to break open the bars would have the red dye on their hands." The sanyasis knew that they were caught and tried to run away from the palace. But the guards caught hold of them.

They were thrown in prison and the King swore that he would never release them. The gold statues were recovered from the forest and Gopal received an award from the King.

Foretelling Or Flattery

King Raja Krishna had two daughters, but he wanted a son. A son, who would become King after he died. Finally his wife, the Queen gave birth to a baby boy. The King was so happy that he ordered everyone in the Kingdom to come and visit his son.

When Gopal the witty barber arrived he looked at the baby boy and said, "Your Highness! This little boy will be even greater than his father." The King was very pleased. When the other courtiers saw this they said to the King, "O King! How can Gopal be so sure that your son will be greater than you? How can he foretell something by just looking at your son? He is trying to flatter you. You ought to punish him." The King knew that Gopal was not the flattering kind, but he decided to find out what Gopal had to say to defend himself. So he asked Gopal, "Gopal! Were you foretelling my son's future or were you trying to flatter me?" Gopal replied, "O King! I have never flattered you and I never will. I could tell

that your son would be greater than you by just observing him." The King was very happy with Gopal's response, but the courtiers were not.

They said to the King, "If he claims to foretell things by just observing them, let's give him a test." The King said, "Why are all of you so jealous of Gopal? I trust him and I know that he is very wise and witty. But to prove to you that he is, I will give him a test. What do you propose I should do?" The courtiers said, "O King, please take two identical pots. Fill one with gold and leave the other empty. Cover both of them with cloth and hang them from a ceiling. When Gopal comes ask him to tell which pot is empty and which is full. He should do so only by observing the pots. He should not touch them."

The King had two identical pots tied to a ceiling in the palace. One pot was filled with gold, while the other was left empty. Then the mouth of each pot was cover with identical pieces of cloth. They were hung from the ceiling with identical pieces of rope.

Then the King called for Gopal. When Gopal arrived the King said, "Gopal, I would like to find out if you could really foretell things by just observing them. I have a small test for you. You see the two pots hanging from the ceiling? One is filled with gold and the other is empty. You have to tell which pot is full and which is empty without touching the pots. If you do that I will know that you are not a flatterer."

Gopal smiled, but inside he was worried. He knew that this was a plan by the jealous courtiers to get rid of him. He thought carefully and then said, "I will not let you down O King!"

Then Gopal walked up to the pots. They were hanging just above his head. He walked around them. Looked up at them and found that they were indeed identical.

Finally he looked up at the pots and sighed. The courtiers began laughing. They thought that Gopal was sighing in despair. One of the courtiers said, "Ha! Look at the wise and intelligent Gopal sighing in despair. He knows that his flattery will not be able to help him this time." Gopal

ignored the comments and looked at the pots once again.

The King waited patiently for Gopal to say something. Gopal walked a few paces away from the pots, stopped and turned around. He looked at the King and said, "O King! The pot on my right is full of gold and the one on my left is empty." The King was not so sure himself, the pots looked so identical. He said, "Gopal! Are you sure?"

Gopal smiled and said, "I am sure O King! As sure as I am that your son will grow up to be greater than his father." The King asked his guards to lower the pots and check. To everyone's surprise, they found that Gopal was right. The pot on the left was empty, and the pot on the right was full of gold.

The King cried out, "Gopal! I am sorry that I listened to those jealous people, I should have trusted you. But please tell me how you were able to tell the difference. Even I was confused because the pots were so identical."

Gopal smiled and said, "It was simple O King! All I did was observe the pots carefully. Although they were tied by identical ropes, one pot was hanging a bit lower than the other. Obviously the weight of the gold in the pot, stretched the rope. But to make sure I did something else. These fools thought that I was sighing in despair. In reality what I did was sigh near the pots so that the wind that came out of my mouth blew into the pots. The one that was empty moved just a little bit. But the one that was full did not move at all."

The King began clapping loudly and shouted, "Gopal! You are truly a gift sent from God! As a reward for your effort I will give you the pot containing the gold."

Gopal returned home a very happy and very rich man thanks to his jealous friends.

Honesty And Dishonesty

Raja Krishna encouraged his courtiers to discuss things. He would join them in debates on various topics. He believed that this would help his people develop their intelligence.

One day the topic of discussion was honesty and dishonesty. Most of the courtiers would wait for Gopal, the witty barber, to speak. He usually had a very different and wise way of looking at things. But one of the senior courtiers was very jealous of Gopal. He felt that the people should listen to him. So before anyone could speak, he said, "O King! I believe that the poor people are dishonest."

The King became angry and said, "How dare you make such a statement. Explain yourself!" The senior courtier realise that he had made a mistake and said, "Oh! ...er..I did not mean it that way your Majesty! What I really meant was that poor people are forced, by their poor financial state, to be dishonest." The King remained silent.

85

Most of the people in the court were quiet rich. They were afraid to say anything about the rich because they would be talking about themselves.

Gopal was the only one in the court who did not come from a rich family, was the only one who objected. He stood up and said, "I disagree O King! I believe that the poor are honest. Rich people like us tend to be more greedy and this makes us dishonest." Before the King could say anything the senior courtier stood up and said, "What rubbish! If you believe that is true, then prove it!"

The King said, "He is right Gopal! Can you prove it?" Gopal smiled and said, "Of course my King! I will be able to prove it, but I will need your help." The King said, "No problem. I will help you in any way I can."

Gopal said, I would like you to give me two small cloth bags filled with gold coins. Then I would like you to appoint four of your guards to watch over the bags." The King was surprised, and said, "That should not be a problem, but what do you intend to do?" Gopal said, "Your

Majesty, the river is the only place in this Kingdom where everyone is equal. Everyone has to go there to have a bath. Of course the rich have a separate area to bathe, further upstream. While the poor have a separate place to bathe downstream. But all of them have to go to the same river. There are two paths leading to the river, one taken by the poor people and one taken by the rich people. What I will do is place a bag of gold coins on each path. We'll find out who is honest enough to return the money."

The King said, "That's a good idea, but what do you want the guards for?" Gopal said, "I want two guards to hide on either side of the path and watch the bag of gold coins. I would like them to see who finds bag first. Then I would like them to follow that person and see what they do with the gold coins." The King called out to four of his most trusted guards and ordered them to do whatever Gopal tells them to.

Late in the evening Gopal went with the guards. He placed one bag of gold coins on the path taken by rich people. He told two of the

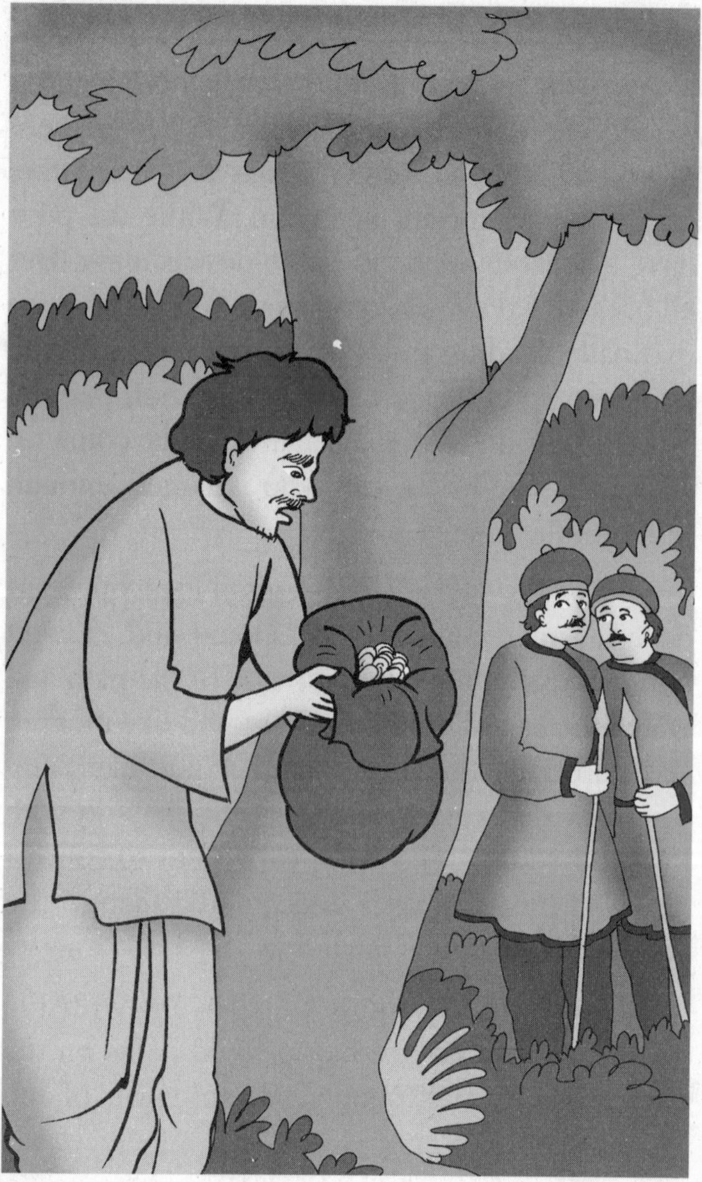

guards to hide in the bushes on either side of the path. Then he went to the path used by the poor people and placed another bag of gold coins on the path. He asked the last two guards to hide in the bushes on either side of the path. He told the guards to follow that person who picks up the bag on each path and find out what they do with the gold coins.

The guards hid themselves in the bushes and fell asleep. They were woken up in the morning by the sound of footsteps. On the path taken by the rich, a wealthy moneylender was the first one to walk along the path. As soon as he spotted the cloth bag, he stopped and picked it up.

When he opened it and saw the gold coins, his eyes opened wide. He quickly looked around to see if anyone was in sight, but there was no one. He said to himself, "What a luck! The Gods are finally smiling on me. They have blessed me with this gold. I will take it home and invest it in my business." The moneylender walked back into town without having his bath. The guards followed the moneylender.

On the other path, the guards were woken up by a happy whistling sound. A poor farmer was walking along the path, whistling a happy tune. Suddenly he spotted the bag and said aloud, "What's this? I wonder who dropped it?" He picked up the bag and opened it. He was shocked to find gold coins inside the bag. More gold coins than he had ever seen in his entire life! He became worried and shouted out, "Hey there! Is there anyone around? Did someone drop a bag of gold coins?" There was no response except the sound of a bird singing in a nearby tree.

The poor farmer said to himself, "I wonder which poor person dropped these gold coins here. It is probably their entire life's savings. When I get back into town I must return it to the King, for they will ask the King to help them find it." Saying that he continued on his path to the river, finished his bath and then walked back into the town. The guards followed him. When he reached the town the poor farmer went straight to the King's palace. He met the King's minister and gave him the bag with the gold coins. He said to the minister, "I found this bag of gold coins on the way to the river. Please keep it and return it to anyone who comes to claim it." The minister gave him a receipt for the gold coins.

After a week the Gopal said to the King, 'O King, you may now call in your guards and ask them what happened to your gold coins." The guards told the King what the moneylender did with the gold coins that he found. Then they told him what the poor farmer did with the gold coins that he found. The King was furious with the moneylender. He shouted to his guards, "Go! Bring me the rich moneylender and the poor farmer at once."

When they arrived the King shouted at the moneylender, "You found a bag of gold coins. Why did you not return them to the minister?" The moneylender said, "O King! I am going through difficult times. Every day I pray that God should give me more money.

I thought that the Gods had finally blessed me with this gift. Beside that, there was no one around. I did look." The King looked at the poor

farmer and said, "Why did you not keep the gold? Why did you return it to the minister? Don't you pray to the Gods for money?"

The poor farmer was afraid, he said, "O King! I thought that the money might belong to someone as poor as me. I thought that it might be their lifetime savings. I don't pray to the Gods for money. I pray that my family and I should be happy with whatever we have."

The King smiled. Gopal stepped forward and said, "Have I proven my point of view O King? As you can see, the poor are honest even though they don't have money. The rich are greedy for more and this makes them dishonest."

The King looked at the jealous courtier and said, "Are you satisfied? He has proven that you are wrong once again. Next time please think before you speak."

The King said to the moneylender, "As punishment for your greed I order you to pay the minister two times the amount of gold coins that you found in the bag." Then he turned to the poor farmer and said, "As a reward for your honesty you can take back the bag of gold coins that you returned to the minister. It is now yours. Go and be happy."

Then the King turned to Gopal and said, "Thanks to you, this court has learned a valuable lesson. I hereby reward you with a bag of gold coins for helping us see the truth." Gopal accepted the reward and went home very happy.

A Royal Dream

One day, King Raja Krishna had a wonderful dream. He dreamed that he had built a statue of himself, Fifty feet high, Covered with gold and precious stones. But the most important thing about the statue in his dream was that it floated in air. Although it was made of solid gold, it floated in air by some miracle.

The next morning King Raja Krishna summoned his courtiers. He said to them, "I have had a wonderful dream. I dreamed that I had built a statue of myself, fifty feet high. Covered with gold and precious stones. A statue that floated in the air. I would like you to get the best craftsmen in the land to build me a statue that floats in the air."

The courtiers were shocked. They knew that it would be easy to build a fifty-foot statue with gold and precious stones. But how could they make the statue float in air? Unable to find a solution one of them found the courage to say to

the King, "Your Majesty, no one has ever built a fifty foot statue that floats in the air. We don't think that it is possible O King!" King Raja Krishna became furious, "How will you know if you don't try?" he shouted.

For many months the King kept pushing his subjects to try and build a statue that floats in the air. But try as they might, it was an impossible task. Finally the courtiers decided to talk to Gopal the witty barber. Gopal seemed to have a solution for every problem. They hoped that Gopal would help them get out of this problem as well.

When they approached Gopal, he thought for a while and then said, "I am honoured to be of assistance to you. Leave me alone for a week and I will make the King forget his dream." The courtiers thanked Gopal and left.

After one week a strange old man came to see the King. He was crying out aloud, "I am ruined. I am ruined. King Raja Krishna has ruined me. He has taken all my money." When the guards heard this they became furious. They caught the old man and took him to prison. On the way the old man continued to scream, "King Raja Krishna has ruined me! King Raja Krishna has ruined me!"

The King heard the old man screaming and said, "Bring him here. I want to hear what he has to say." The guards brought the old man in. The old man fell to his knees and shouted, "O great King Raja Krishna! How could you do this to me? How could you take away all my wealth?"

The King became annoyed and shouted, "Stop it man! I don't know you. And I did not take any of your money. Explain yourself. Why do you think I took away all your money?"

The old man said, "O King, last night I had a dream. In that dream, you and your guards visited my house, broke in and took away all my money. You left me with nothing." The King began laughing and said to the old man, "You are a fool! If you had a dream, how could it possibly be true? Nothing that happens in your dream will come true old man. It is just a dream."

The old man said, "Are you sure? It looked so real." The King smiled and said, "No way old

man! Dreams are just imagination. They will not come true. I have not taken any of your money."

The old man's voice suddenly changed. He smiled and said, "So now you know that you dream about a statue that floats will never be true?" The old man pulled off his beard and moustache. It was a disguise. Beneath the disguise stood Gopal the witty barber. He smiled at the King and bowed before him.

The King burst out laughing and shouted, "Gopal! Gopal! You have tricked me once again. Congratulations! I have realised that my demand to build the statue of my dreams was unfair." The courtiers thanked Gopal for helping them when they were in need.

A Test of Intelligence

The courtiers in King Raja Krishna's court were all scholars. They hated to see a simple barber like Gopal visit the court. But the King trusted Gopal a lot. He respected Gopal's wit and intelligence. And he knew that the scholars in his court could not match Gopal's wit and intelligence. The courtiers were lead by an elderly scholar. He was very jealous of Gopal. He tried several ways to get rid of Gopal, but every time he would fail. Finally one day he came up with a plan to convince the King that Gopal should leave the court.

The jealous courtier said to the King, "O great King Raja Krishna. Your Kingdom has become famous all over. Many people in the other kingdoms talk about how well you rule your Kingdom. They have said that you are a patron of the arts, and that you encourage learned scholars to join your court." King Raja Krishna was very happy to hear this.

The jealous courtier continued, "It is clear that learned scholars have contributed a lot to your court. I would like to request you to invite more learned men to join your court. And while you do that I would like to suggest that you remove anyone who is not a learned scholar from your court. That is the only way you will be able to improve the quality of your Kingdom." Gopal knew that the jealous courtier was attacking him directly. He was the only one in the King's court that was not a scholar. So he said, "I have an objection O King! I don't think that all scholars have intelligence. Even common businessmen and traders have a lot of intelligence. In fact I think that the businessmen and traders possess more intelligence than the scholars."

The jealous courtier shouted, "How dare you! Don't you know that scholars are the ones that run this Kingdom?" Gopal smiled and said, "That may be true Sir, but they need to possess intelligence along with learning. A businessman or a trader needs to possess both in order to survive." The jealous courtier said, "Hah! You are just talking. I bet you will not be able to prove it."

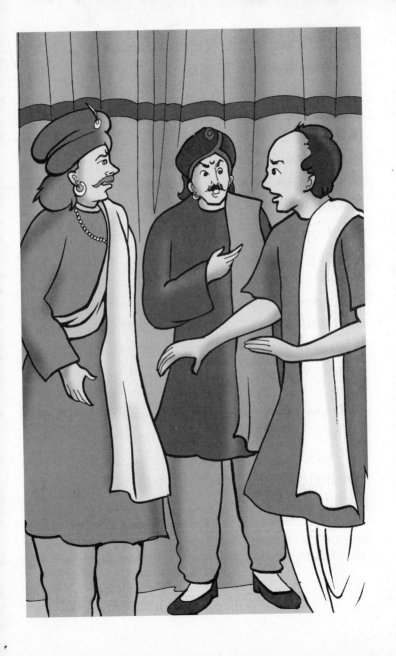

The King looked at Gopal and said, "Will you be able to prove that businessmen are more intelligent than scholars?" Gopal said, "I will definitely try O King. But I will need at least three weeks time." The King said, "Alright. You have three weeks to prove that businessmen are more intelligent than scholars."

Gopal waited for two whole weeks, then one morning, he met the King on his morning walk and said, "O King, I have not forgotten about the challenge you have given me. I will not be able to do it without your help." The King said, "Tell me what you want me to do?" Gopal said, I want you to make an announcement in your court. I want you to ask two people to shave their heads. Tell them that you are collecting hair for an offering to the Gods. I would like you to specifically ask the elderly courtier, who challenged me, to shave his head. Then I would like you to ask a businessman to shave his head also.

Finally I would like you to tell them that you are willing to pay a price for their hair. The King agreed.

So the same day, while the court was in session, the King announced, "People I am making a special offering to the Gods. For this offering I will need two people to shave their heads. A businessman and a scholar. I will collect their hair and offer it to the Gods. Will anyone volunteer to shave their heads?" The entire court was silent. No one wanted to shave their heads. So the King said, "Don't worry I will offer a small reward for the hair." Even then, no one came forward.

So the King looked at the jealous courtier and said, "You are an elderly scholar, why don't you come forward and shave your head. I will give you whatever you ask for the hair." The jealous courtier was worried, he did not want to shave his head, but he wanted the reward. So he said, "Ok your Majesty! I will shave my head.

But I would like you to pay me ten gold coins for my hair." The King smiled and said, "No problem. I will give you the money at once." After the jealous courtier received the ten gold coins he let the King have his head shaved. The King then sent for a businessman who was passing by. When the businessman arrived the King said to him, "I would like you to shave your head. I will pay you ten gold coins for your hair, just like I paid my courtier. " The businessman said, "O great King, I would be honoured to shave my head for your offering.

But there is a small problem. Your courtier does not travel around, so it does not make a difference if he has a baldhead or not. For me things are different. My business is based on trust. If I shave my head people will not recognise me. They will not do business with me. And I will lose more than five thousand gold coins in business." The King looked at him and said, "So? What are you saying?" The businessman replied, "Er…I will shave my head only if you can pay me the five thousand gold coins that I will lose in business O King."

The King said, "Oh! That's all! No problem. I understand your problem, and I know that you will lose business. I will give you five thousand gold coins for your hair." The businessman collected the five thousand gold coins and got

ready to have his head shaved. Just as the court barber was about to shave his head, the businessman said, "Just a minute O King. You have already paid me for my hair, now it belongs to you. So if you shave my head it would be like shaving your own head." The King was shocked. He shouted, "You are right! Now that I have paid you for your hair it belongs to me. So if I shave your head it would be like shaving my head! No way! You may go and keep your hair." The businessman quickly left the palace and never returned.

The King was a bit confused. He called out to Gopal and said, "Ok Gopal! I did what you told me. Now tell me why you asked me to do that?" Gopal smiled and said, "That was to prove to you that businessmen are more intelligent than scholars O King." The King was still confused. He asked Gopal, "What do you mean?" Gopal said, "Your wise and learned scholar only wanted ten gold coins for his hair. But the businessman managed to get five thousand gold coins and keep his hair on. Now you tell me who is more intelligent."

The King began laughing. Finally he realised what Gopal was trying to do. He looked at the poor courtier with his baldhead and said, "Ha! Ha! I'm afraid Gopal has managed to outwit you one more time. He has proved beyond all doubt that businessmen are more intelligent than scholars like you." From that day onwards the jealous courtier never tried to pick on Gopal.

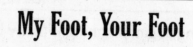

My Foot, Your Foot

One very hot day, Swami Paramanand had a good lunch and decided to take a short afternoon nap. As soon as he lay down to rest, two of the most eager disciples rushed forward to press his legs. In those days, it was considered to be the sacred duty of a disciple to massage his guru's feet.

So although Swami Paramanand protested, the eager disciples, Baloo and Ramaloo, each took hold of one of their guru's feet and began to massage it. Swami Paramanand enjoyed the massage and soon fell into a deep sleep.

As was the case, competition between disciples was fierce. Each disciple was doing his best to outdo the other. Baloo said to Ramaloo, "I know that my master is happy because I am massaging his feet."

Ramaloo shouted back, "Hah! He's happy because I am massaging his feet. I can massage feet better than you."

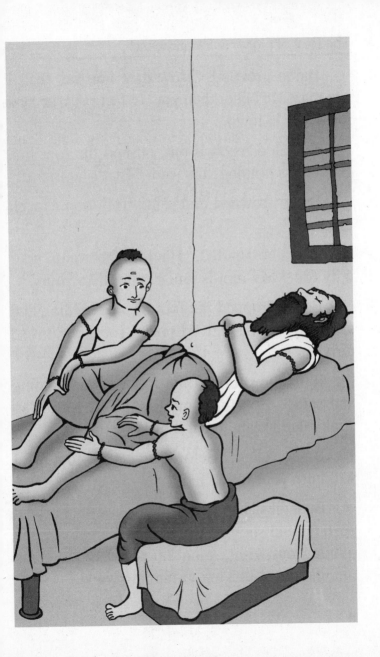

Baloo growled, "How dare you say that. I can massage better than you. In fact I am the best massager in town."

Ramaloo reached out, pushed the foot that Baloo was holding, and said, "That's nonsense!"

Baloo frowned and said, "Hey don't touch my foot!"

Ramaloo snarled, 'Huuh! Who wants your ugly foot? My foot is much better than yours."

Baloo dropped the foot he was holding and said, "My foot is ugly? Look at your foot it is so dirty!"

Ramaloo dropped the foot he was holding and said, "Stop that you idiot. Your foot is so stinky that I want to cut it off!"

Baloo yelled, "Before you cut my foot off, I will burn your rotten foot!"

Both the disciples ran into the nearby kitchen, pushing and shoving each other. Ramaloo came running out with a long knife and Baloo came running out with a log of burning wood.

Both of them rushed into the room and picked up the leg that the other was massaging.

Swami Paramanand was rudely awakened from his sleep to find each disciple pulling at one of his legs. To his horror he found that one was about to cut his leg off while the other was about to burn his other leg.

Swami Paramanand jumped to his feet and shouted at his disciples, "You stupid fools! What do you think you are doing?"

When the disciples told him the reason, Swami Paramanand flew into a rage and beat them up.

In the days of Swami Paramanand, a disciple had to prove that he was loyal to his guru by dedicating his life to the guru. Quite often disciples would fight amongst themselves, to prove that they were more loyal than the other. On other occasions they would get together and plan out a surprise for their guru.

On one such occasion, Swami Paramanand's disciples decided that they had to buy their guru a horse for his birthday. Since the disciples did not work, they got most of their pocket money from people who gave them alms.

The disciples got together and said, "Let's pool in our money and buy our guru a horse. Then he will be able to travel great distances without any problem." All the other disciples agreed. So they collected whatever money they had and left for the market.

On the way to the market, they began to fight with each other. All of them wanted to hold the bag of money since all of them had contributed. So finally one of the disciples said, "Ah! I have an idea. There are five of us here; let's tie five strings to the money-bag and each of us will hold one string. That way we will all carry the money to the market."

The other disciples were very happy. So they tied five strings to the small money-bag and each disciple held on to one string. They made a very strange sight as they hobbled along to the market.

A petty thief who was passing by saw this strange sight and asked them, "Tell me my friends, what are you doing?" Dumloo, the head disciple said, "We are on the way to the market to buy our master a horse. Since all of us contributed money towards the gift, we are sharing the burden of carrying the money to the market."

The thief realised that the disciples were quite stupid, so he decided to trick them. He said, "I'm sorry to tell you this my friends. The money you have will not be enough to buy a grown horse. You will only be able to buy a horse egg." Dumloo thought for a moment and then said, "But what

will our master do with a horse egg?" The thief smiled and said, "That's simple, all you have to do is wait for the egg to hatch and you will get a horse!" The disciples shouted out, "Wonderful! Let's buy a horse egg."

The thief took them to a pumpkin field nearby. He pointed at the biggest pumpkin in the field and said, "There, that one is about to hatch. You can take it after you give me your money." The disciples quickly gave the thief their money and rushed over to pick up the pumpkin. The thief quickly left them and ran away.

The disciples picked up the pumpkin and at once began to fight. Once again, all of them wanted to hold the pumpkin. Dumloo said, "Stop fighting, I have an idea. Each of us will put one hand under the horse egg. So we can carry it together to our master."

So each disciple placed one hand under the pumpkin and they lifted it up together. They kept bumping in to each other but managed to carry the pumpkin a short distance.

Then one of the disciples tripped on a stone and fell. The others lost their balance and the pumpkin went crashing to the ground.

When the pumpkin fell and broke, it disturbed a rabbit that was hiding in a bush nearby. The rabbit ran out of the bush and between the disciple's legs. Dumloo shouted out, "Oh! No! What have we done? We have broken the horse egg and the baby horse has escaped!"

One of the other disciples, Ramaloo shouted, "Don't worry! I'll catch the baby horse."

He ran after the rabbit, but the rabbit was too fast for him and soon vanished into the forest." Ramaloo came back disappointed and said, "I couldn't catch it. We have lost our money and the horse. What a shame!"

They all walked home looking very disappointed.

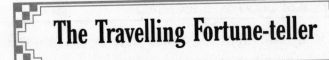

The Travelling Fortune-teller

One day an elderly man came to see Swami Paramanand. He said to him, "O Swami, I have a son who is no good. He tried his hand at farming, but he destroyed all my crops. He tried his hand at being a trader, but he lost all his money. I would like you to accept him as your disciple. I am sure that he will learn a lot from you." Swami Paramanand, was very pleased. He smiled and said, "Of course my friend, I will accept your son as my disciple and I will make him a wise man."

The next day the skinny young man, named Vindhaloo, met Swami Paramanand and became his disciple. Since he was the youngest disciple, he was at once given tasks that all the other disciples did not want to do. He was asked to clean the dishes, wash the clothes and fill water.

Of all the tasks assigned to them, the one task that the disciples hated most was going into the forest to cut wood. The journey into the forest

121

was long, and all the disciples were afraid of wild animals. So when the time came to get some more wood, the senior disciples at once decided that Vindhaloo would have to go into the forest and cut wood.

Poor Vindhaloo had never cut wood in his life. He entered the forest and climbed onto a big branch and began to cut it. Suddenly he heard a voice say, "Hey silly fellow! What are you doing?" Vindhaloo looked down to see a stranger standing under the tree. Vindhaloo shouted back, "Can't you see that I am cutting wood from this tree?"

The stranger laughed and said, "Of course I can see that! But why are you cutting the branch that you are sitting on you idiot! You will fall and hurt yourself!" Vindhaloo became angry. He shouted back, "Don't you call me an idiot! I am a disciple of the famous Swami Paramanand. I can cut wood any way I want to."

The stranger shrugged his shoulders and said, "Ha! Ha! Have it your way. You are going to fall and hurt yourself, just wait and see."

As the stranger walked away, Vindhaloo continued to cut the branch that he was sitting on. Within a few moments the branch broke. Vindhaloo fell to the ground and hurt himself. He looked surprised and shouted, "My goodness! That man must be a fortune-teller. He saw into the future and told me that I was going to fall. I must find him." He got up and limped after the stranger shouting, "Wait a minute Sir! Wait!" The stranger stopped and waited for Vindhaloo.

Vindhaloo rushed up to the stranger and said, "You are a fortune-teller, aren't you? Only a fortune-teller could have known that I was about to fall from the tree." The stranger began to laugh, but Vindhaloo would not give up. He said, "O fortune-teller could you tell me when my guru, Swami Paramanand, will die?" When he managed to stop laughing the stranger said, "Your master will die when his heart stops beating."

Vindhaloo thanked the stranger, picked up the log of wood and ran back to the town. He rushed in to Swami Paramanand's room and told him what had happened.

Then he began to cry as he said, "O Swami! The fortune-teller has also predicted your death. He said that you would die when your heart stops beating."

Swami Paramanand was shocked. He held on to his chest for a few moments and shouted, "Oh! No! I can't feel my heart beating! I think I am going to die!" All the disciples gathered around him and began crying.

Swami Paramanand's wife heard the noise and walked in to see what was happening.

Swami Paramanand called to her saying, "Come here my dear wife. I am about to die."

Swami Paramanand's wife shouted at him, "You silly man! How can you die when you are talking to me? And stop looking for your heart on the right side of your chest. You will find your heart on the left side of your chest!" Swami Paramanand touched the left side of his chest and shouted, "I am alive! I am alive!"